ONE
FAMILY

With deepest thanks to Frances Foster
—G.S.

For Mom and Dad
—B.G.

ISBN 978-1-338-09349-0

12 11 10   20 21

Printed in the U.S.A.   40

First Scholastic printing, September 2016

ONE FAMILY

GEORGE SHANNON · PICTURES BY BLANCA GÓMEZ

SCHOLASTIC INC.

One is one.
One lamp. One clock.
One book to share.

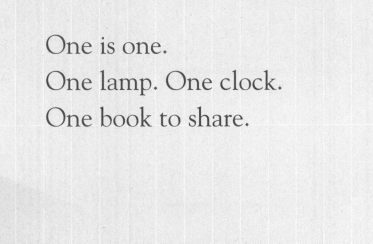

One is two.
One pair of shoes. One team of horses.
One family.

One is three.
One house of bears. One bowl of pears.
One family.

One is four.
One ring of keys. One pile of pups.
One family.

One is five.
One bunch of bananas. One hand of cards.
One family.

One is six.
One line of laundry. One butterfly's legs.
One family.

One is seven.
One bouquet of blooms. One flock of birds.
One family.

One is eight.
One box of crayons. One row of ducks.
One family.

One is nine.
One flight of stairs. One collection of rocks.
One family.

One is ten.
One batch of cookies. One shelf of books.
One family.

One is one and everyone.
One earth. One world.
One family.

1

2

3

6

7

8

4

5

8
CRAYONS

9

10